ALAS, BABYLON

by
Pat Frank

Student Packet

Written by
Pat Watson

Contains masters for:

2 Prereading Activities
4 Vocabulary Activities
1 Study Guide
1 Literary Analysis Activity
3 Character Analysis Activities
3 Comprehension Activities
4 Quizzes
2 Final Tests (2 levels)
Alternative Assessment

PLUS

Detailed Answer Key
and Scoring Rubric

Note

The 2005 Harper Perennial Modern Classics paperback edition of the book, © 1959 by Pat Frank, was used to prepare this guide. The page references may differ in other editions. Novel ISBN: 0-06-074187-2

Please note: This novel deals with sensitive, mature issues, e.g., nuclear war and its aftermath, savagery, death. Please assess the appropriateness of this book for the age level and maturity of your students prior to reading and discussing it with them.

ISBN-10: 1-58130-551-6
ISBN-13: 978-1-58130-551-7

To order, contact your local school supply store, or—

Novel Units, Inc.
P.O. Box 97
Bulverde, TX 78163-0097

Web site: www.novelunits.com

Lori Mammen, Editorial Director
Andrea M. Harris, Production Manager/Production Specialist
Taylor Henderson, Product Development Specialist
Heather M. Marnan, Product Development Specialist
Suzanne K. Mammen, Curriculum Specialist
Pamela Rayfield, Product Development Specialist
Jill Reed, Product Development Specialist
Adrienne Speer, Production Specialist

Name _____

Directions: Rank the following in the order you think most necessary for survival following a nuclear disaster, with 12 being the least important. Write two or three sentences explaining your #1 choice.

_____ Mechanical modes of communication

_____ Food

_____ Tools

_____ Salt

_____ Housing

_____ Water

_____ Fire

_____ Companionship

_____ Electric generator

_____ Money

_____ Medical supplies

_____ Underground shelter

_____

_____

_____

_____

_____

_____

_____

Getting the "Lay of the Land"

Directions: Prepare for reading by answering the following short-answer questions.

1. Who is the author?

   _____

2. What does the title suggest to you about the book?

   _____

   _____

   _____

   _____

3. When was the book first copyrighted?

   _____

4. How many pages are there in the book?

   _____

5. Thumb through the book. Read three pages—one from near the beginning, one from near the middle, and one from near the end. What predictions can you make about the book?

   _____

   _____

   _____

   _____

   _____

6. What does the cover suggest to you about the book?

   _____

   _____

   _____

   _____

judiciously (1)	irascible (2)	voyeur (5)	commiserated (15)
audacious (16)	subversive (23)	cerebrate (30)	capitulation (31)
untenable (31)	miasma (32)	tactical (32)	antipathy (40)
affront (40)	cataclysm (43)	artesian (50)	saturnine (54)
hypertension (57)	vector (72)	incongruously (84)	ballistic missiles (90)

Directions: If the underlined word in each of the following sentences is used correctly, answer yes; if it is used incorrectly, answer no. For any incorrect word, rewrite the sentence on the back of this page so that the word is used correctly.

1. A perceptive, unbiased judge <u>judiciously</u> presides over each trial.   YES   NO

2. An <u>irascible</u> old man is adaptable and pleasant in every situation.   YES   NO

3. People will usually welcome a <u>voyeur</u> into their gated community.   YES   NO

4. Our nation as a whole <u>commiserated</u> with victims of Hurricane Katrina.   YES   NO

5. An <u>audacious</u> child will back away from almost any challenge.   YES   NO

6. Spies are noted for their use of <u>subversive</u> tactics.   YES   NO

7. Most children love to <u>cerebrate</u> holidays.   YES   NO

8. During a war, each side tries to bring the other to the point of <u>capitulation</u>.   YES   NO

9. <u>Untenable</u> military bases are easily defended.   YES   NO

10. Rumors of war often create a <u>miasma</u> among the people.   YES   NO

11. A <u>tactical</u> approach to a problem always produces fear and uncertainty.   YES   NO

12. <u>Antipathy</u> between two people is mutually beneficial.   YES   NO

13. It is difficult to respond to an <u>affront</u> with kindness and understanding.   YES   NO

14. A major earthquake creates a <u>cataclysm</u>.   YES   NO

15. <u>Artesian</u> water flows freely without being pumped.   YES   NO

16. A <u>saturnine</u> guest is guaranteed to be the life of the party.   YES   NO

17. Someone who suffers from severe <u>hypertension</u> needs immediate medical attention.   YES   NO

18. A <u>vector</u> officiates at weddings and funerals.   YES   NO

19. A person who is dressed <u>incongruously</u> will be out of place at a formal dinner.   YES   NO

20. <u>Ballistic missiles</u> are aimed at or before the time of launching.   YES   NO

Name _____

inexplicably (91)	contrails (93)	undulating (97)	atavistic (98)
gesticulating (100)	cravenly (101)	corpulent (103)	dissipation (107)
effrontery (113)	fiduciary (115)	holocaust (118)	improvident (122)
infamy (126)	moratorium (127)	pugnacious (140)	fastidious (147)
noxious (151)	septic (158)	macadam (164)	unorthodox (167)
emaciated (174)			

Directions: Choose the word or phrase in each list closest in meaning to the vocabulary word. Select eight of the words and use them in a rhyming or free verse poem.

_____ 1. **inexplicably:** (a) understandably (b) cautiously (c) mysteriously (d) closely

_____ 2. **contrails:** (a) vapor trails (b) cattails (c) railroad ties (d) mountainous trails

_____ 3. **undulating:** (a) calculating (b) regulating (c) rolling (d) doubting

_____ 4. **atavistic:** (a) attractive (b) primitive (c) visible (d) modern

_____ 5. **gesticulating:** (a) creating (b) regurgitating (c) signaling (d) singing

_____ 6. **cravenly:** (a) cowardly (b) boldly (c) encouragingly (d) cautiously

_____ 7. **corpulent:** (a) military officer (b) corpuscle damage (c) slim (d) fat

_____ 8. **dissipation:** (a) uprightness (b) debauchery (c) precipitation (d) distribution

_____ 9. **effrontery:** (a) forward (b) respect (c) impudence (d) cowardice

_____ 10. **fiduciary:** (a) holding in trust (b) leading to distrust (c) governmental collapse (d) superfluous

_____ 11. **holocaust:** (a) sacred ceremony (b) unjust cause (c) massive destruction (d) peaceful settlement

_____ 12. **improvident:** (a) negligent (b) careful (c) unproven (d) influential

_____ 13. **infamy:** (a) honor (b) familial honor (c) resolution (d) atrocity

_____ 14. **moratorium:** (a) mortal fear (b) public assistance (c) suspension (d) mausoleum

_____ 15. **pugnacious:** (a) snub-nosed (b) confrontational (c) peaceable (d) obstinate

_____ 16. **fastidious:** (a) particular (b) lenient (c) swift (d) silly

_____ 17. **noxious:** (a) mischievous (b) harmless (c) deadly (d) gaseous

_____ 18. **septic:** (a) healthy (b) infected (c) skeptical (d) staid

_____ 19. **macadam:** (a) pavement (b) large boulders (c) type of nut (d) majestic mountains

_____ 20. **unorthodox:** (a) traditional (b) religious (c) study of orthodontics (d) unconventional

_____ 21. **emaciated:** (a) rotund (b) shrunken (c) emancipated (d) earnest

Vocabulary Chart

inured (180)	maelstrom (181)	barter (182)	disparity (184)
insidious (186)	remunerative (188)	marauders (192)	ludicrously (193)
capriciously (195)	avocation (200)	highwaymen (210)	boondoggle (214)
martial law (221)	paradoxical (227)	vicissitudes (230)	cryptic (231)
palavers (236)			

Directions: Write each vocabulary word in the left-hand column of the chart. Complete the chart by placing a check mark in the column that best describes your familiarity with each word. Working with a partner, find and read the line where each word appears in the story. Find the meaning of each word in the dictionary. Together with your partner, choose ten of the words checked in the last column. On a separate sheet of paper, use each of those words in a sentence.

Vocabulary Word	I Can Define	I Have Seen/Heard	New Word For Me

Name _____

august (253)	decamped (259)	imprudent (266)	sortie (270)
wantonly (272)	immutable (281)	acumen (286)	malleable (287)
chagrined (298)	translucent (309)	tertiary (314)	

Directions: Complete the following analogies with the correct vocabulary word.

1. SECRETLY is to CLANDESTINELY as UNJUSTIFIABLY is to _____.

2. LOVED is to CHERISHED as ANNOYED is to _____.

3. CONCRETE is to INSUBSTANTIAL as DISPUTABLE is to _____.

4. AGREEMENT is to TREATY as RAID is to _____.

5. SINGLE is to SOLITARY as THIRD is to _____.

6. TEDIOUS is to STIMULATING as CAREFUL is to _____.

7. COMPLICATED is to CONVOLUTED as MAJESTIC is to _____.

8. IGNORED is to NOTICED as STAYED is to _____.

9. TAUT is to SLACK as INFLEXIBLE is to _____.

10. SKILL is to EXPERTISE as WISDOM is to _____.

11. FEASIBLE is to IMPOSSIBLE as OPAQUE is to _____.

Name _____

Directions: Answer the following questions on a separate sheet of paper. Starred questions indicate thought or opinion. Use your answers in class discussions, for writing assignments, and to review for tests.

Chapters 1–2, pp. 1–37

1. *Identify the setting (place and date). Why do you think this is important to this novel?

2. Who is the protagonist? Briefly describe him at the beginning of the novel.

3. Identify the following characters and give two adjectives for each one: (a) Florence Wechek, (b) Alice Cooksey, (c) Preacher Henry, (d) Lib McGovern, (e) Two-Tone, (f) Malachai, (g) Missouri, (h) Dan Gunn.

4. Why is Fort Repose called "Randy's town"?

5. What information does Mark Bragg's telegram to Randy contain? How does he conclude the telegram? How does this relate to Randy and Mark's conversation the previous Christmas?

6. *Explain whether you agree or disagree with the statement, "Censorship and thought control can exist only in secrecy and darkness" (p. 23).

7. Identify two changes at McCoy Air Base that indicate preparations for a nuclear attack.

8. What does Mark tell Randy about the impending war?

9. How has the United States learned about Russia's plans to attack the United States?

10. What two reasons does Mark give for believing war is imminent?

11. What does Mark give Randy before they part? Why?

Chapters 3–4, pp. 39–90

1. *Who is Edgar Quisenberry? Why does he have a grudge against Randy Bragg? What do you think this indicates about Quisenberry?

2. *What survival preparations does Randy make? What else do you think he needs to do?

3. Who is Malachai Henry? How does Randy feel about him and his family? How does Malachai react to the news of a possible nuclear attack?

4. *What does the Henry family have that hardly anyone else in Fort Repose has? Why do you think this information is important?

5. Briefly summarize the relationship between Randy and Lib McGovern. How do her parents feel about Randy?

6. *How do the following react to the news of an impending nuclear attack: Lib, Dan Gunn, Bill McGovern? Whose reaction do you think is most logical? Why?

7. Why does Dan Gunn have financial difficulties? How has this affected him?

8. What physical illness does Lavinia McCoy have? Why does this concern Dan Gunn after he hears of a possible nuclear attack?

9. *How do Mark, Helen, and the children react to their parting? What do you think this reveals about each of them?

10. What seaport does Ensign Cobb inadvertently strike? Why is this important to the United States/Soviet Union relations?

11. What does Mark Bragg convince General Hawker to do? Why is this important?

12. What types of enemy weapons are headed for the United States?

Chapter 5, pp. 91–122

1. What initial signs indicate to Randy that a nuclear attack has occurred?

2. What causes Peyton's temporary blindness?

3. How does Ben Franklin demonstrate his training in preparation for a nuclear attack?

4. *What does Randy discover on his way to Fort Repose? How does he react? What do you think this reveals about him?

5. *Briefly describe the scene when Randy gets to Fort Repose. How do you think people in your town would react in a similar situation?

6. What does Florence discover when she initially tries to send a telegram?

7. What does Edgar Quisenberry demand of Florence? What happens when she attempts to do this? What does this indicate?

8. *What is Edgar's "first and vital error"? Why do you think this is relevant?

9. Why does Edgar close the bank? What is his excuse?

10. *What does Edgar believe the phrase, "the end of civilization as we know it" means? How does this affect him? What is his final act? What do you think this "solution" reveals about Edgar?

Chapters 6–7, pp. 123–177

1. *What is the significance of the label "The Day"? What other labels would you apply to this day in history?

2. *What items are on Helen's "must" list? What does Randy add to the list? Which item do you think is the most important? Why?

3. Who is now the Acting President of the United States? Why is this significant? What does she relate about the attack?

4. Who is Admiral Hazzard? Why does Randy want to visit with him?

5. How does Dan think Randy will respond to the crisis?

6. Does Dan believe Fort Repose is in danger of severe radiation poisoning? Why or why not?

7. *Briefly explain life without electricity. What would be your biggest adjustment to loss of electric power?

8. How does Randy solve the water problem in his house? Who helps him?

9. Identify three ways in which Fort Repose has changed since The Day.

10. What information does the announcement from the Civil Defense Headquarters give about Florida? about Omaha? How does this affect the community on River Road?

11. What causes Lavinia McGovern's death? Where do they bury her? What is Randy's rationale for suggesting they do so?

12. Why do Dan and the McGoverns move into Randy's house?

Chapter 8, pp. 179–211

1. *Identify three things Randy misses since The Day. What does he miss the most? What would you miss most in similar circumstances? Why?

2. What are the staple foods in the diet of the community on River Road?

3. What does Randy believe they must do for the Henrys? Why?

4. Who is affected with radiation poisoning? Whom does Randy suspect as the source?

5. Why is Alice Cooksey the only person from the River Road community who continues with her regular work at the same location as before The Day? How does she feel about her work? Why?

6. *How does the bartering system affect racism in Fort Repose and the surrounding area? How do you think a situation like this would affect racism today?

7. *What do you think is the most urgent appeal posted on the bulletin board? Why?

8. *Where do Randy and Dan go to see Pete Hernandez? What is your impression of this area?

9. Briefly describe Rita Hernandez. What is her hobby? How do she and Randy react to each other?

10. What do Dan and Randy discover is the source of the radiation poisoning? What does Dan think will happen to Pete?

11. What do Randy and Dan discover about Porky Logan? about Bill Cullen?

Chapter 9, pp. 213–244

1. Why does Dan believe they must bury Porky in a lead-lined coffin? How does Bubba Offenhaus react to Randy's request? How does Randy persuade him to agree?

2. *How does Randy convince the men to help carry Porky's coffin? What does this incident cause Randy to realize about himself? Why do you think this is significant?

3. What gives Randy the legal right to be the authority in Fort Repose?

4. Briefly explain what Helen fantasizes about Randy. Who explains the incident to him, and what is the diagnosis?

5. *Explain what you think Peyton's statement, "If I grow up..." implies.

6. Why are Ben Franklin and Caleb standing guard? What weapons do they use?

7. Why does Sam Hazzard think the communication between Big Rock and Sky Queen is significant?

8. *What do Sam, Randy, and Lib learn about health and living conditions in the following countries: France, the Soviet Union, the United States, Canada, and Mexico? What countries are sending aid? What do you think this message infers?

9. What happens to Dan? Who brings him out of shock?

10. What does Ben Franklin kill? How does he react, and why?

Chapter 10–11, pp. 245–284

1. Where had Dan been before the highwaymen attacked him? Why did he go there?

2. How many perpetrators were involved in the attack? Why did Dan stop? How did he get home?

3. *What does Randy vow to do to the perpetrators? What does Dan think is more important? What do you think this reveals about each of them?

4. *How does Rita Hernandez help in the pursuit of the highwaymen? How does Randy persuade her to do so? What do you think this reveals about her?

5. When do Lib and Randy marry? Who performs the ceremony? Identify two ways this differs from most traditional weddings.

6. Why does Malachai think he should drive the truck when they pursue the highwaymen? Who convinces Randy to allow him to do so? What happens to Malachai?

7. How many highwaymen die in the initial attack? What happens to the other one?

8. What does Dan prepare to do to try to save Malachai's life? Who assists him?

9. *What is Bragg's Troop? When is it formed? How many men initially volunteer? Why do you think this is important?

Chapters 12–13, pp. 285–316

1. What two things happen to the River Road community in May? How does this affect them?

2. How do living conditions improve in June? Why is August the month of disaster?

3. How does Dan solve the problem of anesthesia? How does Alice help him with this? Who is the first patient to benefit from this?

4. How does the lack of salt affect the community? How does Randy solve the problem?

5. How does Peyton solve the problem of the lack of fish? What motivates her to do so?

6. *Identify two positive changes that take place on River Road in the months of September and October. Which one of these would mean the most to you? Why?

7. What news does Dan bring at the end of October? Why is this so important?

8. *Why does Randy tell Peyton he would pin a medal on her if he had one? How do you think this makes Peyton feel?

9. What does the airplane drop to the people in Fort Repose? Give two reasons this is important to the community on River Road.

10. When does the helicopter come? Identify the Colonel who is on board and briefly state what he reveals about the following: the area in and around Fort Repose, the effect of the nuclear attack on the United States, Mark Bragg, who won the war.

11. *Explain the symbolism of the "thousand-year night."

Character Attribute Chart

Directions: Choose five characters from the book. List their names in the left-hand boxes. Fill in the other boxes for each character with requested information, including a two-word description before and one year after "The Day."

Character	Description Before	Description After	Strongest Attribute	Significance to the Story

Name _____

Sociogram

Directions: A sociogram shows the relationship between characters in a story. Complete the sociogram below by writing a word to describe the relationships between the characters. Remember, relationships go both ways, so each line requires a descriptive word.

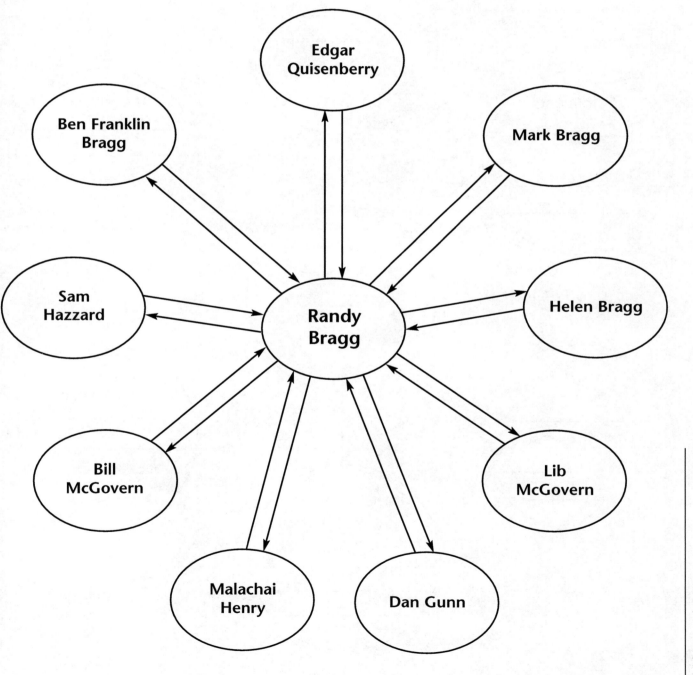

Character Web

Directions: Complete the attribute web below by filling in information specific to Randy.

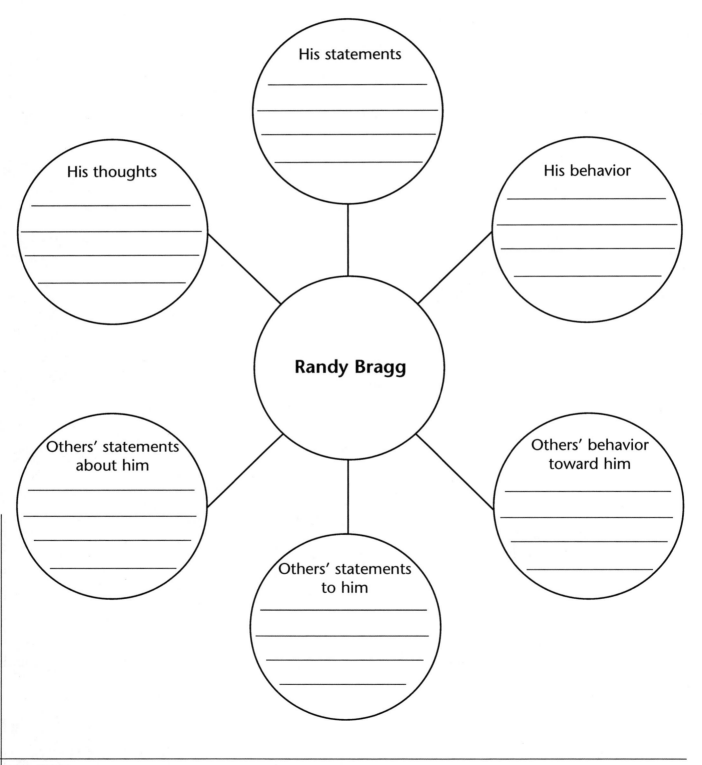

Name _____

Inference Flow Chart

Directions: Fill in the boxes of the flow chart with the events portrayed in the story. In the ovals beneath, state what emotions and feelings are inferred.

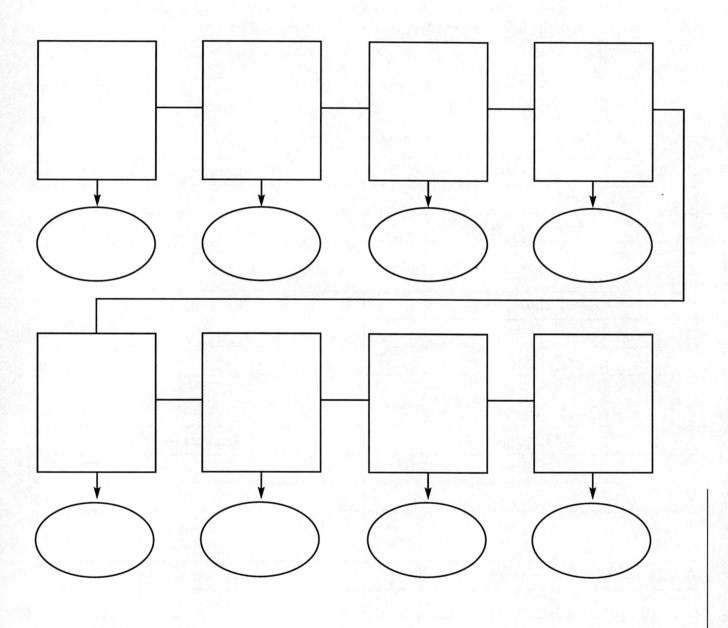

Conflict

The **conflict** of a story is the struggle between two people or two forces. There are four main types of conflict: person vs. person, person vs. nature, person vs. society, or person vs. self.

Directions: The characters in *Alas, Babylon* experience a variety of conflicts in the story. In the space provided, list four conflicts the characters experience and how they resolve these conflicts.

person vs. person

Conflict	Resolution

person vs. nature

Conflict	Resolution

person vs. society

Conflict	Resolution

person vs. self

Conflict	Resolution

Name _____

Story Map

Characters _____

_____

Setting

Time and Place _____

_____

↓

Problem

Problem _____

_____

_____

↓

Goal

Goal _____

_____

_____

↓

Episodes

Beginning ⟶ Development ⟶ Outcome

_____

_____

_____

_____

↓

Resolution

Resolution _____

_____

_____

_____

Solving Problems

Directions: List six problems the characters in the novel face. Then complete the rest of the chart.

Problem	Character's Solution	Outcome without Character's Solution

Name _____

A. True/False

_____ 1. Florence Wechek suspects Randy Bragg of spying on her.

_____ 2. Randy has a prosperous, thriving career as a lawyer.

_____ 3. Mark Bragg sends his wife and children to Randy the day after the nuclear attack.

_____ 4. An American Air Force pilot deliberately fires on the Syrian port of Latakia.

_____ 5. The government issues a red alert because at least four ballistic missiles are headed toward the United States.

B. Fill in the Blanks

6. The setting for the novel is _____.

7. Randy's current girlfriend is _____.

8. Mark and Randy first hear the phrase "Alas, Babylon" from

_____.

9. The United States government learns about Russia's plans for a nuclear attack from

_____.

10. _____ is the first person Randy tells about the imminent

nuclear attack.

C. Open-Ended Comprehension: On the lines below, explain the significance of the novel's setting.

_____

_____

_____

_____

_____

_____

Name _____

A. Short Answer: Write brief answers to the following questions on a separate sheet of paper.

1. What are the first two signs that make Randy aware of a nuclear attack?
2. What happens to Peyton during the nuclear attack?
3. Identify two effects of the nuclear attack in Fort Repose and surrounding areas.
4. What excuse does Edgar Quisenberry give for closing the bank?
5. What does Quisenberry do to avoid facing a world without money?
6. What do the people in Fort Repose call the day of the first nuclear attack?
7. What does the message from the Acting President of the United States reveal about the President, Vice President, and other high-ranking government officials?
8. How does Randy supply water for his house?
9. What happens to the Fort Repose Chief of Police?
10. What causes Lavinia McGovern's death?

B. Open-Ended Comprehension: On the lines below, compare/contrast Randy Bragg's and Edgar Quisenberry's reactions to an urgent situation.

_____

_____

_____

_____

_____

_____

_____

_____

_____

A. True/False

_____ 1. Four months after The Day, Randy misses coffee most of all.

_____ 2. Randy refuses to allow Ben Franklin to stand guard at the Henrys' place.

_____ 3. Dan Gunn attributes three cases of radiation poisoning to delayed fallout.

_____ 4. Alice Cooksey is the only person on River Road to continue with her regular work.

_____ 5. Bartering becomes the primary method to obtain food and other supplies.

_____ 6. Pete Hernandez is the primary person responsible for spreading radiation poisoning.

_____ 7. Randy threatens five men with arrest if they refuse to help bury Porky Logan.

_____ 8. Randy's handling of Porky's funeral legalizes his authority in Fort Repose.

_____ 9. Sam Hazzard compares the Fall of the United States with the Fall of the Third Reich.

_____ 10. Highwaymen savagely beat Dan Gunn.

B. Open-Ended Comprehension: On the lines below, explain Randy's rationale for becoming the authority in Fort Repose and its surrounding areas.

_____

_____

_____

_____

_____

_____

_____

_____

_____

_____

Name _____

A. Fill in the Blanks

1. The highwaymen take Dan's medical supplies and _____.

2. _____ supplies a truck and gasoline for the pursuit of the highwaymen.

3. _____ performs Randy and Lib's wedding ceremony.

4. _____ drives the pursuit truck.

5. _____ [number] highwaymen die in the initial confrontation.

6. The surviving highwayman dies by _____.

B. Matching: Match each character with the correct identification.

_____ 7. Randy Bragg   a. restores music to the Bragg household

_____ 8. Malachai Henry   b. brings news of the war to River Road

_____ 9. Dan Gunn   c. discovers a source of salt

_____ 10. Peyton Bragg   d. learns hypnotism for medicinal purposes

_____ 11. Paul Hart   e. dies

C. Open-Ended Comprehension: On the lines below, explain the significance of the final phrase, "...Randy turned away to face the thousand-year night."

_____

_____

_____

_____

_____

_____

_____

A. Identification: Match each character with the correct description.

____ 1. Randy Bragg

____ 2. Mark Bragg

____ 3. Dan Gunn

____ 4. Elizabeth McGovern

____ 5. Bill McGovern

____ 6. Malachai Henry

____ 7. Sam Hazzard

____ 8. Porky Logan

____ 9. Bubba Offenhaus

____ 10. Alice Cooksey

a. overweight, greedy politician

b. retiree who finds a new purpose for living

c. sends family away to protect them

d. protagonist; assumes leadership in Fort Repose

e. self-centered owner of local mortuary

f. retired military officer; owns short-wave radio

g. conscientious librarian

h. intelligent, trustworthy; dies defending the law

i. capable, ingenious doctor

j. attractive, loyal; protagonist's girlfriend

B. Multiple Choice: Choose the BEST answer.

____ 11. Fort Repose is important as the setting because
   a. its citizens have learned survival skills
   b. it has enough money to sustain a crisis
   c. the Chief of Police is able to enforce the law
   d. of its distance from the nuclear attack targets

____ 12. All BUT which of the following is true of Florence Wechek?
   a. spreads malicious gossip
   b. best friend of Alice Cooksey
   c. suspects Randy of spying on her
   d. manager of the local telegraph office

____ 13. Randy's initial reaction to Mark's telegram is
   a. a sick feeling
   b. an "I told you so" attitude
   c. refusal to believe its message
   d. to immediately alert the director of Civil Defense

____ 14. Edgar Quisenberry initially refuses to cash Mark's $5,000 check to Randy because
   a. the bank is low on funds
   b. Randy arrives five minutes after closing time
   c. he doesn't believe Mark has that much money
   d. he has a long-standing grudge against their father, Judge Bragg

_____ 15. The first person Randy tells about the imminent nuclear attack is
    a. Dan Gunn
    b. Porky Logan
    c. Lib McGovern
    d. Malachai Henry

_____ 16. At the beginning of the novel, Dan Gunn is cynical and disheartened because
    a. he has no friends in Fort Repose
    b. the World Health Organization rejected him
    c. a bitter divorce leaves him with high alimony payments
    d. he has a difficult time collecting money from his patients

_____ 17. Helen Bragg does not want to go to Fort Repose because she
    a. must leave her children behind
    b. is afraid Mark no longer loves her
    c. feels like she is deserting her husband
    d. does not believe Randy is trustworthy

_____ 18. Which of the following is NOT true of the Fort Repose area following the initial nuclear attack?
    a. heavy, erratic traffic
    b. relatively calm guests at the Riverside Inn
    c. escaped convicts walking along the highway
    d. telegraph office allowed to send only official defense emergency messages

_____ 19. Florence Wechek and Alice Cooksey react to the nuclear attack by
    a. becoming hysterical
    b. going to their jobs in town as usual
    c. trying to get an airline ticket to leave
    d. seeking Randy's advice about what to do

_____ 20. Edgar Quisenberry's solution to facing life without money is to
    a. commit suicide
    b. barter for food and supplies
    c. get in his car and leave town
    d. hoard all the money he can until the financial problem improves

_____ 21. The inability to purchase necessities regardless of how much money people have is attributed to
    a. previous foolish spending
    b. the implacable law of scarcity
    c. the law of diminishing returns
    d. frivolous waste of commodities

_____ 22. Survivors of the nuclear attack in Fort Repose refer to the attack as
   a. H-Day
   b. The Day
   c. Hell Day
   d. That Day

_____ 23. The message from the Acting President of the United States reveals that
   a. the United States is winning the war
   b. the President and Vice President are dead
   c. everything possible is being done to save the nation's power plants
   d. she has assumed this role because the President has been flown out of the country

_____ 24. Sam Hazzard is able to interpret many of the short-wave radio messages because
   a. he is a retired Navy officer
   b. he is an advisor at the Naval Academy
   c. his son gives him additional information
   d. he has a reference book to decipher terms

_____ 25. The attack on Dan's clinic results in
   a. Dan's savage beating
   b. the death of the Chief of Police
   c. the loss of all Dan's medical supplies
   d. Dan's determination to leave Fort Repose

_____ 26. Lavinia McGovern's death is attributed to
   a. diabetes
   b. hypertension
   c. cardiac arrest
   d. radiation poisoning

_____ 27. Ben Franklin is allowed to stand guard with a gun at
   a. the Henrys' place
   b. the citrus orchard
   c. the medical clinic
   d. the McGovern house

_____ 28. The bartering system in Fort Repose
   a. is a failure
   b. increases racial tension
   c. minimizes racial prejudice
   d. bans African Americans from participating

_____ 29. Dan and Randy discover the source of the radiation poisoning to be
    a. jewelry Pete Hernandez stole
    b. lures and hooks from Bill Cullen's tackle box
    c. jewelry Rita Hernandez has been using to barter
    d. jewelry Porky Logan seized on the day of the nuclear attack

_____ 30. Five volunteers agree to carry Porky Logan's coffin in response to
    a. Dan's concern
    b. Bubba Offenhaus' appeal
    c. Randy's threat with a gun
    d. his wife's plea for sympathy

_____ 31. Randy's authority in Fort Repose becomes legal
    a. when the people elect him sheriff
    b. after he forms a band of vigilantes
    c. when he discovers his ancestor's diary giving the Bragg family this right
    d. because the Acting President of the U.S. authorizes Reserve officers to assume this position

_____ 32. Lib attributes Helen's advances toward Randy to
    a. psychosis
    b. jealousy of Peyton
    c. a prior deep-seated attraction to him
    d. transference to him of her love for Mark

_____ 33. Highwaymen savagely beat Dan and steal
    a. only his car
    b. only his supply of whiskey
    c. only the narcotics from his bag
    d. his medical supplies and his car

_____ 34. For the pursuit of the highwaymen, Rita Hernandez supplies
    a. money for a truck
    b. a truck and gasoline
    c. food for Randy's group
    d. camouflage clothing for the group

_____ 35. Casualties during the fight between the highwaymen and the pursuers include
    a. two highwaymen
    b. two men and one woman
    c. Malachai and one highwayman
    d. Malachai and three highwaymen

_____ 36. The public hanging of the surviving highwayman results in
    a. the surrender of two other criminals
    b. a public outcry against capital punishment
    c. seven volunteer enlistments in Bragg's Troop
    d. Randy's resignation as the town's legal authority

_____ 37. Randy discovers the solution to the community's salt problem
    a. in his ancestor's diary
    b. by learning to distill water
    c. when he is sailing down the river
    d. in a book Alice brings him from the library

_____ 38. Which of the following does NOT happen during September and October to encourage the community on River Road?
    a. Fruit and meat become readily available.
    b. Dan delivers his first healthy post-Day baby.
    c. Peyton discovers much-needed items in the attic.
    d. Alice Cooksey organizes a school for the children.

_____ 39. After his arrival, Colonel Paul Hart reveals that
    a. Mark Bragg has survived
    b. the United States has won the war
    c. electric power should be restored within a year
    d. the United States is still a first-class world power

_____ 40. In response to Hart's offer to take anyone who wishes to go away from Fort Repose,
    a. no one wants to leave
    b. Sam Hazzard chooses to go
    c. Bill McGovern decides to go
    d. Helen feels she must go for her children's sake

C. Open-Ended Short Answer Questions: Respond to the following on a separate sheet of paper. Support your answers with evidence from the novel.

(a) Explain the significance of the title, *Alas, Babylon.*

(b) Explain what the River Road community does to help the Henrys and why they do so.

D. Essay: Respond to one of the following on a separate sheet of paper.

(a) Discuss the author's development of the theme of survival.

(b) Discuss what you think to be the author's rationale for writing this book.

Name _____

A. Identification, Part I: Give two adjectives that describe each character before The Day, two that describe him or her one year later, and a short phrase that explains his or her role in the survival of the community.

1. Randy Bragg:

2. Dan Gunn:

3. Two-Tone Henry:

4. Bill McGovern:

5. Sam Hazzard:

6. Alice Cooksey:

7. Florence Wechek:

8. Lib McGovern:

9. Helen Bragg:

10. Ben Franklin Bragg:

11. Peyton Bragg:

B. Identification, Part II: Write two adjectives that describe each of the following characters and a short phrase that explains what happens to him or her.

12. Malachai Henry: _____

_____

13. Edgar Quisenberry: _____

_____

14. Mark Bragg: _____

_____

15. Rita Hernandez: _____

_____

C. Multiple Choice: Choose the BEST answer.

_____ 16. Mark Bragg believes the United States is unprepared for a Soviet nuclear attack
because this country
a. has no nuclear weapons
b. is busy fighting another war
c. spends too much money building national parks
d. has failed to keep up with the Soviet Union in a space-ship world

© Novel Units, Inc.

_____ 17. An American pilot's inadvertent attack on a Syrian port is important to the plot because
    a. American planes are based there
    b. Syria is an ally of the Soviet Union
    c. Syria is an ally of the United States
    d. the attack detonates nuclear weapons in the port

_____ 18. The message from the Acting President of the United States following the nuclear attack reveals all BUT which of the following?
    a. The nation can expect other attacks.
    b. Several hundred enemy air bases have been destroyed.
    c. SAC headquarters in Omaha is now the temporary seat of government.
    d. Neither the President, the Vice President, nor any other Cabinet member survived the attack.

_____ 19. The bartering system in Fort Repose does all BUT which of the following?
    a. increases racial tension
    b. minimizes racial prejudice
    c. reveals the people's desperation
    d. provides a place to exchange news

_____ 20. Which two of the Seven Deadly Sins directly relate to the deaths of Edgar Quisenberry and Porky Logan?
    a. Pride/Sloth
    b. Envy/Anger
    c. Pride/Greed
    d. Greed/Gluttony

_____ 21. Randy Bragg initially assumes the leadership role in Fort Repose because he
    a. is available and reliable
    b. has served in the military
    c. is appointed by the Chief of Police
    d. manipulates the people into selecting him

_____ 22. A short-wave radio message reveals all BUT which of the following?
    a. The Soviet Union's Maritime Provinces no longer exist.
    b. The "Big Three" now consists of China, India, and Japan.
    c. Several hundred thousand French refugees face starvation.
    d. A smallpox epidemic rages in the U.S., Canada, and Mexico.

____ 23. Rita Hernandez's primary motivation for supplying a truck and gasoline for the pursuit of the highwaymen is
   a. self-preservation
   b. love for Randy Bragg
   c. loyalty to her country
   d. concern for the welfare of the citizens of Fort Repose

____ 24. All BUT which of the following occurs in the denouement?
   a. Helen learns of Mark's death.
   b. Fort Repose is declared free of contamination.
   c. The community of River Road learns that the United States won the war.
   d. Citizens of Fort Repose are told they can expect restored electric power within a year.

____ 25. The author wrote *Alas, Babylon* to reflect his observations on all BUT which of the following?
   a. U.S. military priorities
   b. U.S. government bureaucracy
   c. the fallacies of a particular political party
   d. the threat of nuclear war and its aftermath

D. Quotes: Match each quote with the correct speaker.

____ 26. "Censorship and thought control can exist only in secrecy and darkness."
____ 27. "Some nations and some people melt in the heat of crisis and come apart like fat in the pan."
____ 28. "They don't mind losing ten or twenty million people...because people, per se, are only pawns, and expendable."
____ 29. "We're going to have to be tough. We're going to have to be catfish."
____ 30. "Nobody's going to use atomic bombs, just like nobody used gas in the last war."

   a. Mark Bragg

   b. Bill McGovern

   c. Dan Gunn

   d. Alice Cooksey

   e. Randy Bragg

E. Open-Ended Short Answer Questions: Write a response to each item. Support your answers with evidence from the novel.

31. Explain the symbolism of the novel's title.

_____

_____

32. Explain the importance of the Henry family to the survival of the community on River Road.

_____

_____

33. Explain the "implacable law of scarcity."

_____

_____

34. Explain the significance of the Acting President's reference to the "day of infamy."

_____

_____

35. Explain why the novel ends with, "...Randy turned away to face the thousand-year night."

_____

_____

F. Essay: On a separate sheet of paper, complete one of the following in a well-developed essay. Use specific evidence from the novel to support your answers.

(a) Trace the development of Randy Bragg's character in his "journey." Be sure to include what he is like at the beginning and at the end of the novel.

(b) Explain the symbolism of darkness throughout the novel.

(c) Explain the importance of both the time and place of the setting.

Name _____

Alternative Assessment

Directions: Write a response to five of the following items. Answers to #1–#5 must be well-developed paragraphs and must cite examples from the book.

1. Compare/contrast Randy Bragg's and Edgar Quisenberry's reactions to the emergencies created by the nuclear attack.

2. Explain the cause/effect of the interdependence of the people on River Road.

3. Explain the literal and figurative significance of the highwaymen's savage attack on Dan Gunn.

4. Explain whether you think the author's message is optimistic or pessimistic.

5. Correlate the statement "With the use of the hydrogen bomb, the Christian era was dead, and with it must die the tradition of the Good Samaritan" (p. 98) with two characters whose lives demonstrate this concept and two whose lives do not.

6. Write a poem of 18–24 lines that retells the story of The Day.

7. Write a metaphorical poem of at least 12 lines about wealth as it relates to the novel.

8. Write your own plan for survival in the event of a nuclear attack on this country.

Answer Key

Activities #1–#2: Answers will vary.

Activity #3: (Corrected sentences will vary.) 1. Yes 2. No 3. No 4. Yes 5. No 6. Yes 7. No 8. Yes 9. No 10. Yes 11. No 12. No 13. Yes 14. Yes 15. Yes 16. No 17. Yes 18. No 19. Yes 20. Yes

Activity #4: 1. c 2. a 3. c 4. b 5. c 6. a 7. d 8. b 9. c 10. a 11. c 12. a 13. d 14. c 15. b 16. a 17. c 18. b 19. a 20. d 21. b

Activity #5: Answers will vary.

Activity #6: 1. wantonly 2. chagrined 3. immutable 4. sortie 5. tertiary 6. imprudent 7. august 8. decamped 9. malleable 10. acumen 11. translucent

Study Guide

Chapters 1–2, pp. 1–37: 1. Fort Repose, Florida; 1959; Answers will vary (Foreword, pp. ix, 1). 2. Randy Bragg; lawyer, works sporadically, lives on family's land, indifferent (pp. 4–8) 3. (a) manages telegraph office; suspicious, lonely (b) librarian; conscientious, friendly (c) pastor of church; concerned, helpful (d) Randy's girlfriend; lovely, affluent (e) Missouri's husband; lazy, alcoholic (f) preacher's son; industrious, intelligent (g) Randy's housekeeper; perceptive, loyal (h) doctor; cynical, disheartened (pp. 1–26) 4. His ancestor founded it (pp. 11–12). 5. wants to meet him at McCoy, is sending his family to Fort Repose; "Alas, Babylon"; had discussed the possibility of nuclear attack (pp. 13–15) 6. Answers will vary. 7. tightened security, half of the planes dispersed elsewhere, civilians evacuated (pp. 26–28) 8. Russia has powerful fleet in Mediterranean and plans to fire nuclear weapons toward U.S. and other targets (pp. 31–33) 9. from a Russian general (p. 33) 10. Navy is trying to track four unidentified submarines; He has been recalled to SAC headquarters (pp. 33–34). 11. check for $5,000; for family's reserve and to buy supplies (pp. 35–36)

Chapters 3–4, pp. 39–90: 1. owner of bank; calls him Fisheye, grudge against his father; Answers will vary (pp. 39–41). 2. stocks up on food supplies and liquor; Answers will vary (pp. 44–46). 3. Randy's neighbor and yardman; closer to him than anyone else except Lib; isn't surprised (pp. 47–50) 4. artesian water; Answers will vary (p. 50). 5. have been dating two months, falling in love; dislike him (pp. 51–53, 72–74) 6. Lib: shocked but trusts Randy; Dan: angry but not surprised; agrees to stock up on medical supplies; Bill: doesn't believe him; Answers will vary (pp. 57–59, 74–76). 7. must make large alimony payments; is bitter and depressed (p. 55) 8. diabetes; may lose electric power and can't refrigerate her essential insulin (pp. 56, 59) 9. Mark—resolved; Helen—feels like a deserter; children— Ben Franklin understands necessity, Peyton is carefree; Answers will vary (pp. 65–67). 10. Syrian port of Latakia; Syria is ally of Soviet Union (pp. 69–72) 11. ask for release of weapons; gives them 90 seconds of extra time (pp. 88–89) 12. ballistic missiles (p. 90)

Chapter 5, pp. 91–122: 1. shaking of house, loud booming sound, glow in sky (p. 91) 2. watching nuclear explosion (pp. 94–95) 3. fills available basins with water, opens the windows (pp. 94–97) 4. wrecked car, dead woman; initially drives away but returns to see if he can help; Answers will vary (pp. 97–98). 5. escaped convicts, traffic piling up, people seem lost; Answers will vary (pp. 100–106). 6. only emergency messages allowed (pp. 109–110) 7. to be allowed to send a telegram to Federal Reserve Bank; response begins but is cut off; weapon has hit Jacksonville (pp. 110–112) 8. to run the bank himself; Answers will vary (p. 113). 9. running low on funds and wants plenty for himself; government order (p. 116) 10. the end of money; doesn't want to live without money; commits suicide; Answers will vary (pp. 120–122).

Chapters 6–7, pp. 123–177: 1. symbolizes division between everything that came before and after the first day of the attack; Answers will vary (p. 123). 2. dishwasher and laundry soap, paper napkins, toilet paper; ammunition for guns; Answers will vary (pp. 125, 130). 3. Mrs. Josephine Vanbruuker- Brown; her superiors are all dead; many cities destroyed, untold numbers killed, U.S. badly hurt but not defeated (pp. 125–126) 4. retired Navy Admiral, Randy's neighbor; knows he has a short-wave radio (pp. 128–129) 5. will meet the challenge and harden (p. 133) 6. no; far enough away to receive little fallout (pp. 134–135) 7. oil furnaces die because no electricity to spark them; no radios unless battery-powered or in cars; no common household appliances; no electricity to pump water so no functioning bathrooms; Answers will vary (p. 145). 8. pipes artesian water from Henry place; Malachai and Two-Tone (pp. 147–151) 9. litter everywhere, no commerce, few people, no women on streets, lack of law enforcement (pp. 153–155) 10. entire state is a Contaminated Zone; 50-mile radius around Omaha contaminated; realize widespread devastation, have little hope that Mark is alive (pp. 161–163) 11. diabetes; her yard; would require too much gasoline to take her remains to town (pp. 165, 172–174) 12. Dan: clinic destroyed, hotel has no running water or food; McGoverns: no heat or food in their house (pp. 159–160, 170–171)

Chapter 8, pp. 179–211: 1. smooth shave, music, cigarettes; coffee; Answers will vary (pp. 179–180). 2. citrus, fish, eggs (p. 183) 3. guard their place; to keep predators from stealing their chickens and pigs (pp. 184–185) 4. Porky Logan, Bill Cullen, Pete Hernandez; Porky (pp. 186–187) 5. library still open; excited, challenged; People use the library more than ever before (pp. 187–188). 6. Hunger and survival erase racial lines; Answers will vary (p. 190). 7. Answers will vary. 8. Pistolville; Answers will vary (p. 198). 9. strikingly attractive, seductive; men; Rita: tries to rekindle affair; Randy: evades her and won't barter with her (pp. 200–203) 10. jewelry Porky seized near Miami on The Day; die from leukemia (pp. 204–207) 11. dead; wife has run off with jewelry; He is dying (pp. 208–210).

Chapter 9, pp. 213–244: 1. to safely dispose of contaminated jewelry with him; disagrees because of expense; reminds him of his role as Deputy Director of Civil Defense (pp. 213–214) 2. draws a gun; He is the accepted authority. Answers will vary (pp. 215–217). 3. Acting President authorizes Reserve officers to preserve public safety, and Randy is an officer (p. 221). 4. that he is Mark; Lib; transference of affections due to stress (pp. 222–224) 5. Answers will vary. 6. to try to kill the predator that is stealing the Henrys' chickens and pigs; Ben Franklin: shotgun, Caleb: spear (pp. 227–228) 7. U.S. and Soviets both still fighting (p. 231) 8. France: several hundred thousand refugees face starvation; Soviet Union: typhus epidemic; U.S., Canada, Mexico: smallpox epidemic; China, Japan, India, Argentina; Answers will vary (pp. 232–233). 9. savagely beaten and robbed; Helen (pp. 239–241) 10. dog; sobs because he thought it was a wolf (pp. 242–244)

Chapters 10–11, pp. 245–284: 1. at the Sunbury farm; children have typhoid (pp. 247–248) 2. four; to help woman who pretended she was in pain; walking and crawling (pp. 249–251) 3. find them and kill them; do something about typhoid in the river; Answers will vary (p. 252). 4. lets them use her truck and gasoline; reminds her that she will be an easy target when she is alone; Answers will vary (pp. 260–261). 5. Easter Sunday morning; Preacher Henry; the way the bride's father and best man are dressed, matron of honor takes ring from her own hand (pp. 265–268) 6. because they will be more likely to attack a black man; Sam Hazzard; dies (pp. 270–271, 281) 7. three; hanged (pp. 276–278, 283) 8. operate with steak knives; Helen (pp. 280–281) 9. volunteers to assist Randy in keeping order; after the public hanging; seven; Answers will vary (p. 283).

Chapters 12–13, pp. 285–316: 1. radio flares and dies, gasoline vanishes, communication with outside world cut off; must walk or ride a bicycle (p. 285) 2. vegetables mature, produce first whiskey in still; run out of vegetables, fruit, and salt, and fish stop biting (pp. 285–288) 3. learns hypnosis; brings him teaching books from library; Ben Franklin (pp. 286–287) 4. people sweat their salt away, grow weak and ill; discovers source of salt by reading his ancestor's diary; brings salt from Blue Crab Pool (pp. 289–292, 297–299) 5. decides to find out why fish aren't biting from Preacher Henry, takes Florence's goldfish for bait, goes out on river in Randy's boat, and catches fish; feels rejected and wants to be a hero (pp. 293–299) 6. schooling resumes, new crop of oranges ripens, flock of chickens increases, sow has litter of pigs, ducks, turkeys, and quail are abundant; Answers will vary (pp. 299–300). 7. has delivered first healthy post-Day baby; indicates that the human race will continue (pp. 300–301) 8. because she finds a hand-cranked phonograph and records, treadle sewing machine, kerosene lamps, and razors in the attic; Answers will vary (pp. 301–303). 9. fliers announcing a survey to detect contamination in the area and the impending arrival of a helicopter; proves U.S. government still functions, and paper serves as toilet paper (p. 307) 10. December; Paul Hart; Fort Repose: free of contamination; U.S.: Denver is the capital, Orlando has disappeared, geography of some areas completely changed, will take possibly a thousand years to restore contaminated zones, the U.S. has become a second- or third-class world power; Mark is dead. We won (pp. 311–314). 11. Answers will vary.

Note: Answers to Activities #7–#13 will vary. The following are suggested responses.

Activity #7: (1) Randy Bragg: lackadaisical, nonassertive; dynamic, authoritative; leadership; protagonist (2) Dan Gunn: cynical, miserable; effectual, confident; medical knowledge; doctor (3) Bill McGovern: dejected, sarcastic; energetic, innovative; intelligence; expertise helps others survive (4) Sam Hazzard: secluded, indignant; optimistic, inventive; stability; invents sails to power boats (5) Malachai Henry: intelligent, reserved; confident, sociable; innovation; helps everyone, dies to uphold law

Activity #8: Center: Randy Bragg; (1) Edgar Quisenberry: conciliatory, antagonistic (2) Mark Bragg: affectionate, confident (3) Helen Bragg: concerned, secure (4) Lib McGovern: loving, devoted (5) Dan Gunn: congenial, affable (6) Malachai Henry: appreciation, respect (7) Bill McGovern: uncertain, aversion (8) Sam Hazzard: admiration, trust (9) Ben Franklin Bragg: affectionate, trusting

Activity #9: Randy Bragg—His thoughts: apprehension about nuclear war, concern for his household; His statements: about Highwaymen, "I'll find them and kill them." His behavior: assumes leadership, restores law and order; Others' statements about him: Florence, after telling Alice he is a Peeping Tom, "But I saw him at it!" (p. 24); Others' statements to him: Dan, "I think you're going to harden." (p. 133); Others' behavior toward him: respect, look to him for leadership

Activity #10: (1) Mark tells Randy about impending nuclear attack: Randy feels sick. (2) Randy tells Lib and Dan: shocked, anxious (3) First nuclear weapons strike: fearful, apprehensive, uncertain (4) Electric power ceases: worried, doubtful, inventive (5) Chaotic conditions in Fort Repose: fearful, uncivilized (6) Savage attack on Dan and others: angry, resolute, practical (7) Confrontation with highwaymen: fearful, determined, brave (8) Helicopter arrives: hopeful, dismayed, unwavering

Activity #11: (1) Randy Bragg vs. Edgar Quisenberry: deep-seated resentment, refusal to cash check; Randy tricks him into doing so. (2) Peyton vs. decline of fish; discovers from Preacher Henry how to catch them (3) Randy vs. men of Fort Repose; refusal to help bury Porky Logan; gets them to do so by threatening with a gun (4) Bill McGovern vs. himself: feels unwanted and powerless; finds new will to live by working for others

Activity #12: Characters: Randy Bragg, Dan Gunn, Lib McGovern, Helen Bragg, Malachai Henry, others on River Road; Time and Place; Fort Repose, Florida; 1959; Problem: need to survive nuclear attack; Goal: become self-sufficient, establish law and order; Beginning: nuclear missiles attack all around Fort Repose in Florida; Development: People cooperatively and innovatively discover ways to survive; Randy assumes leadership. Outcome: survive for the year, develop camaraderie and close-knit community; Resolution: helicopter arrives and reveals details of war; members of River Road community decide to stay

Activity #13: Problem (1) no fresh water; pipe artesian water into homes; forced to use impure river water, disease (2) money useless; barter for food and supplies; more starvation (3) chaos and disorder in Fort Repose; Randy assumes leadership; conditions worsen, leading to more crime (4) highwaymen attack Dan and others: posse finds them and destroys them; continuing robbery and murder (5) Dan has no anesthesia; learns hypnosis; unable to do some medical procedures (6) no salt; Randy discovers location and brings salt; continuing health problems

Quiz #1: A. 1. T (pp. 4–6) 2. F (p. 12) 3. F (pp. 14–16) 4. F (pp. 71–72) 5. T (p. 90) **B.** 6. Fort Repose, Florida; 1959 (p. 1) 7. Lib McGovern (p. 7) 8. Preacher Henry (p. 14) 9. a Russian general (p. 32) 10. Malachai Henry (pp. 47–49) **C.** Answers will vary. Refer to the scoring rubric on page 40 of this guide.

Quiz #2: A. 1. shaking and swaying, powerful rumble (p. 91) 2. temporarily blinded (pp. 94–95) 3. heavy erratic traffic, confusion, accidents, anger, fear, escaped convicts (pp. 100–106) 4. forced to close by the government (p. 116) 5. commits suicide (p. 122) 6. The Day (p. 123) 7. All are dead (p. 127). 8. pipes artesian water from Henry place (pp. 150–151) 9. murdered trying to defend medical clinic (pp. 157–158) 10. diabetes, lack of insulin (p. 165) **B.** Answers will vary. Refer to the scoring rubric on page 40 of this guide.

Quiz #3: A. 1. T (p. 180) 2. F (pp. 184–185) 3. F (p. 186) 4. T (p. 187) 5. T (pp. 190–194) 6. F (pp. 204–205) 7. F (pp. 215–216) 8. F (p. 221) 9. F (p. 236) 10. T (p. 239) **B.** Answers will vary. Refer to the scoring rubric on page 40 of this guide.

Quiz #4: A. 1. his car (pp. 250–251) 2. Rita Hernandez (pp. 260–261) 3. Preacher Henry (p. 266) 4. Malachai (p. 270) 5. Three (pp. 276–277) 6. hanging (p. 284) **B.** 7. c (p. 292) 8. e (p. 281) 9. d (pp. 286–287) 10. a (pp. 302–303) 11. b (pp. 310–316) **C.** Answers will vary. Refer to the scoring rubric on page 40 of this guide.

Final Test, Level One: A. 1. d 2. c 3. i 4. j 5. b 6. h 7. f 8. a 9. e 10. g **B.** 11. d (p. 1, inference) 12. a (pp. 1–4) 13. a (p. 14) 14. d (pp. 40–42) 15. d (p. 49) 16. c (pp. 55–56) 17. c (p. 65) 18. b (pp. 100–108) 19. b (pp. 107–108) 20. a (pp. 121–122) 21. b (p. 117) 22. b (p. 123) 23. b (p. 127) 24. a (pp. 138, 141) 25. b (p. 157) 26. a (p. 165) 27. a (p. 184) 28. c (pp. 190–191) 29. d (pp. 204–205) 30. c (pp. 215–216) 31. d (p. 221) 32. d (pp. 222–224) 33. d (p. 240) 34. b (pp. 256–261) 35. d (pp. 276–277, 281) 36. c (p. 283) 37. a (p. 292) 38. d (pp. 299–303) 39. b (p. 316) 40. a (pp. 314–316) **C. & D.** Answers will vary. Refer to the scoring rubric on page 40 of this guide.

Final Test, Level Two: A. Answers will vary. Suggestions: 1. indifferent, uninvolved; energetic, resourceful; becomes the leader 2. cynical, discouraged; positive, ingenious; doctor 3. lazy, intoxicated; active, innovative; invents still 4. unproductive, sarcastic; industrious, optimistic; mechanic, supports Randy 5. private, lonely; involved, cooperative; supervises boats 6. disheartened, realistic; enthusiastic, busy; provides learning material 7. suspicious, forlorn; cheerful, busy; keeps records, helps Alice 8. lovely, affluent; poor, encouraging; Randy's confidant and lover 9. faithful, conscientious; compliant, industrious; cares for family 10. well-informed, brave; capable, enthusiastic; helps stand guard 11. naive, delightful; knowledgeable, resourceful; discovers treasures in attic
B. 12. intelligent, ingenious; dies defending the law 13. egotistical, materialistic; commits suicide 14. concerned, devoted; dies in first attack 15. self-centered, seductive; left alone when Pete dies
C. 16. d (p. 16) 17. b (pp. 71–72, 77) 18. c (pp. 126–127) 19. a (pp. 190–191) 20. c (inference) 21. a (inference) 22. a (pp. 232–233) 23. a (pp. 259–261) 24. d (pp. 313–316) 25. c (inference)
D. 26. d (p. 23) 27. c (p. 133) 28. a (p. 32) 29. e (p. 177) 30. b (p. 75) **E.** Answers will vary. Suggestions: 31. The phrase refers to the destruction of biblical Babylon in one hour. It has become Mark and Randy's synonym for disaster. Nuclear attacks devastate the United States in less than an hour. 32. Their artesian water is piped into the houses on River Road; they provide eggs, chickens, pigs, and vegetables for everyone. Malachai dies in pursuit of the highwaymen. Missouri cleans for and takes care of everyone. 33. With the nuclear attack, deliveries of supplies cease. Supplies quickly diminish, and people can't purchase necessities regardless of how much money they have. 34. President Roosevelt called the day the Japanese bombed Pearl Harbor the "Day of Infamy." The Acting President refers to the day of the nuclear attack as a "darker day of infamy," implying

unimaginable devastation. 35. Power plants have been destroyed, and it may take a thousand years to restore modern technology to Fort Repose; the nation faces the darkness of death, disease, and destruction. **F.** Answers will vary. Refer to the scoring rubric on page 40 of this guide.

Alternative Assessment: Answers will vary, but should include the following information. 1. Randy: realistic, is determined to survive, assumes leadership, becomes stronger, instrumental in survival of others; Edgar: weak, manipulative, materialistic, incapable of surviving without money, kills himself, leaves wife to survive alone 2. Cause: lack of food; Effect: work together and share fish, vegetables, and fruit; Cause: lack of pure water; Effect: pipe artesian water to homes; Cause: shortage of gasoline; Effect: use Henrys' old car, as it consumes less fuel 3. Literal: savagery of those who prey on others, danger of being alone in troubled time and area; Figurative: attack against law and order, symbolic of lawlessness that attempts to prevail when regular legal system breaks down 4. Optimistic: The United States can and will survive a nuclear attack; Pessimistic: The United States is unprepared for nuclear war. 5. Those who do: Randy, Malachai; Those who do not: Porky Logan, Edgar Quisenberry; 6.–8.: Answers will vary.

Linking Novel Units® Student Packets to National and State Reading Assessments

During the past several years, an increasing number of students have faced some form of state-mandated competency testing in reading. Many states now administer state-developed assessments to measure the skills and knowledge emphasized in their particular reading curriculum. This Novel Units® guide includes open-ended comprehension questions that correlate with state-mandated reading assessments. The rubric below provides important information for evaluating responses to open-ended comprehension questions. Teachers may also use scoring rubrics provided for their own state's competency test.

Scoring Rubric for Open-Ended Items

3-Exemplary	Thorough, complete ideas/information Clear organization throughout Logical reasoning/conclusions Thorough understanding of reading task Accurate, complete response
2-Sufficient	Many relevant ideas/pieces of information Clear organization throughout most of response Minor problems in logical reasoning/conclusions General understanding of reading task Generally accurate and complete response
1-Partially Sufficient	Minimally relevant ideas/information Obvious gaps in organization Obvious problems in logical reasoning/conclusions Minimal understanding of reading task Inaccuracies/incomplete response
0-Insufficient	Irrelevant ideas/information No coherent organization Major problems in logical reasoning/conclusions Little or no understanding of reading task Generally inaccurate/incomplete response